The World of Rod McKuen

Books by Rod McKuen

Stanyan Street and Other Sorrows
Listen to the Warm
Lonesome Cities

The World of Rod McKuen

The World of Rod McKuen

Words and Music by Rod McKuen

Photographs by Helen Miljakovich

Piano Arrangements by Ben Kendall

Random House   **New York**

Second Printing

Copyright © 1968 by Rod McKuen and Helen Miljakovich
Copyright © 1963, 1965, 1966, 1967 by Stanyan Music Co.
Copyright © 1967, 1968, by Editions Chanson Co.

Library of Congress Catalog Card Number: 68-29390
Manufactured in the United States of America

Cover photo by Photo Media Ltd.

Designed by David Paul and Phoebe Rodbart

For Joe Smith

A NOTE

I write to find out about myself; what makes me turn. I never wanted to be a writer—or planned to be one. I have always been a singer who needed songs that reflected how he felt about himself and his surroundings in order to make his performance of them believable. In desperation I had to write my own material. There just weren't enough songs reflecting *me,* written by other people.

This book contains twenty-two songs—all of them personal, some of them I think are pretty good. Ben Kendall's arrangements have captured the songs as I wanted them to be. The photographs were taken by Helen Miljakovich. She has invaded, perhaps, a bit more of my world than I'd planned. But she's done so with kindness, intelligence and talent.

People ask me what I like to do best—write poetry, songs, sing, whatever. I don't play favorites. My work, if I can call it that, is all I am. What I write and perform is an extension of myself. *The World of Rod McKuen* is limited to what I know and what I continue to find out about myself and the people and places and thoughts that take me out of myself and into the larger world. I'm not very far into that world yet, but I'm a little further along than I was yesterday.

These songs and this book are a gift to those who've been able to make me have a world at all.

Rod McKuen
London, June 1968

Contents

The World
of Rod McKuen

I'm Strong But I Like Roses

Slowly with feeling

Once in ev-'ry life - time, A lit - tle bird may come; A - lone and for - got - ten, knocked down by the sun. Ev -'ry man may choose to turn and walk a - way, Or take the bird in - to his hand

and bid him stay.   A man may like ros - es,

and still be big and strong;   And what is life with - out   a

lit - tle bird's   song.   I'M STRONG_ BUT I LIKE

ROS - ES   And if a bird should come,

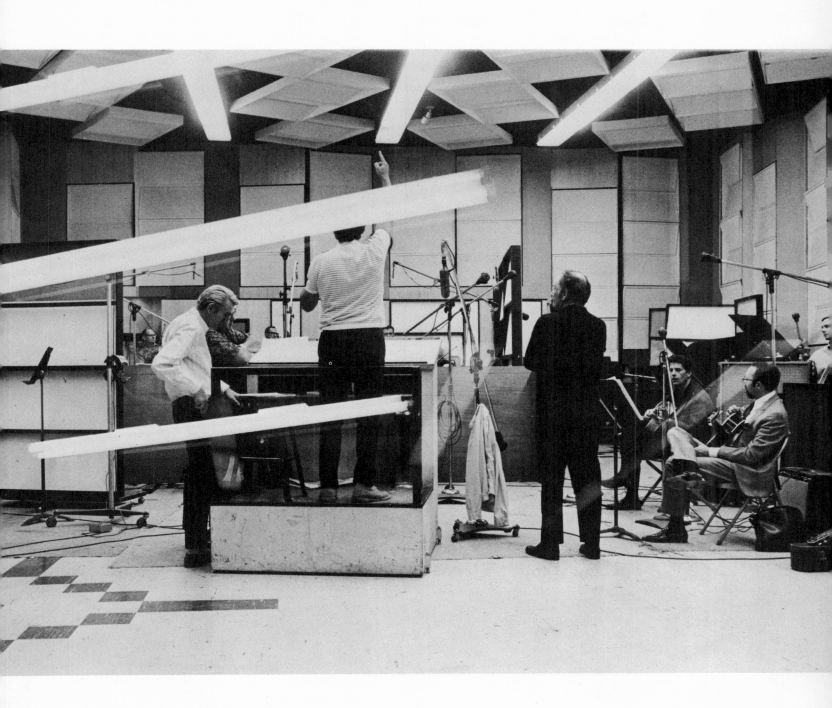

People Change

blows; Give your love, get heart-break in ex-change, Aft - er

all, PEO - PLE CHANGE. You

know as well as I, With just the same old sky,

A bird gets might-y rest-less and has to __ fly.

PEO - PLE CHANGE, Now you're

back, If there's some -thing my old smile seems to lack; I don't

love you now, but if you think it strange, Aft - er all, PEO-PLE

CHANGE. _____

a tempo

14

To Die in Summertime

si-lence, with-out a sin-gle sound, To touch the earth as gen-tly as a dead leaf, when it

hits the ground. To leave be-hind a mem-'ry soft as sum-mer-time, For those one

loves and has to leave be-hind. _____ To

fold as soft-ly as the grass blades fold, When wild things tram-ple them on morn-ings damp and

cold.   To leave be‑hind a   fra‑grance, car‑ried   on   the wind for those one loves and will

nev‑er see a‑gain._____   TO DIE IN   SUM‑MER‑TIME,   or not to

die at all,   While I'm still run‑ning,—   While I'm still run‑ning for‑ward,—

While I still own my own mind,   I want to go in sum‑mer‑time.

1.
TO DIE IN

2.

Where Are We Now?

for Charlotte Brennan

23

WHERE ___ ARE WE NOW? A thou - sand miles a - part.

What ___ have we now? What have we now?

Not e - ven love e - nough to break each oth - er's heart.

To Coda

D.S. al Coda

Coda

We sit with - in the gloom of just this lit - tle room,

Won - der - ing ___ WHERE ARE WE NOW? ___

25

Love, Let Me Not Hunger

Verse:

The bum-ble bee goes from the rose to the mar-i - gold, Then goes back to the rose; The cat-er-pil-lar climbs each rib-bon of vine, 'Cause e - ven the cat-er-pil-lar knows. The day's so warm, you would-n't dare touch it, If it lay down by your side; So come to me, come to me, My arms are o - pen wide.

Slowly

Chorus:

LOVE LET ME NOT HUN-GER, ___ I've been a-lone so long;

How can a lit-tle taste of wine be wrong? ___ We'll

not get an-y young-er, Come lis-ten to my song;

And if you've had a hun-ger, Per-haps you'll sing a-long. The

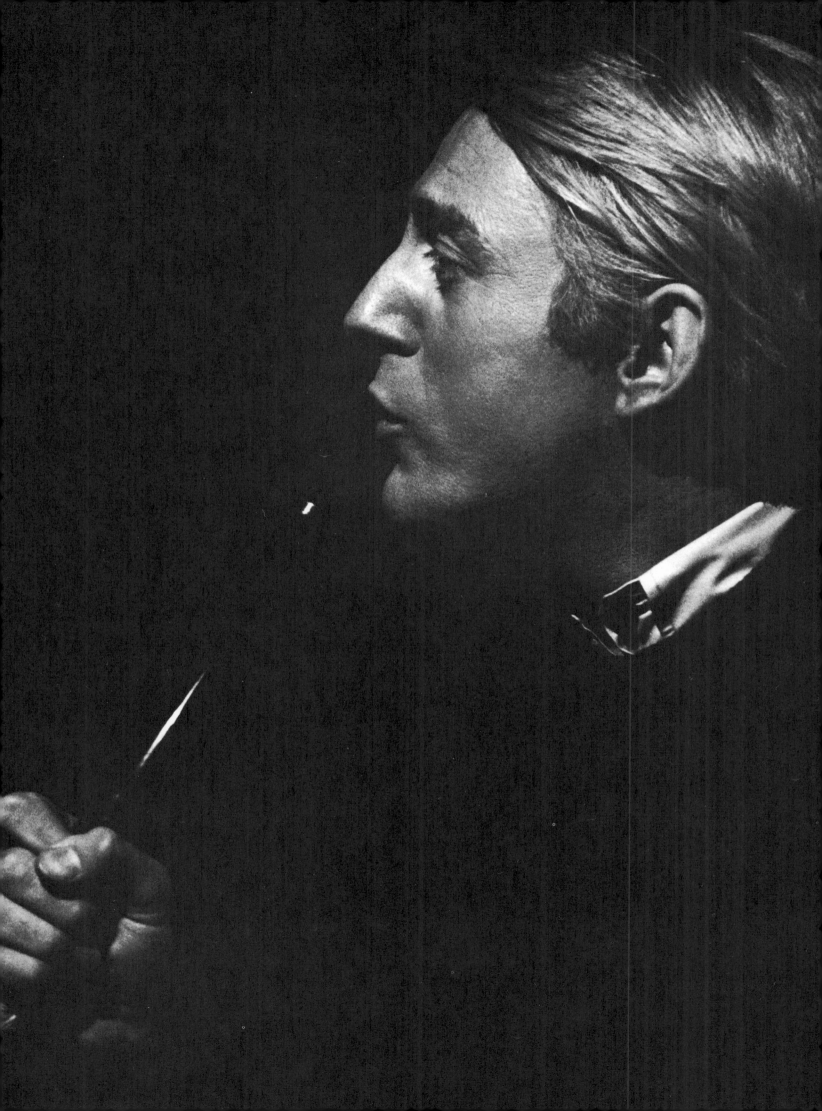

Listen to the Warm

for Phillip and Jeannie Martin

The Beautiful Strangers

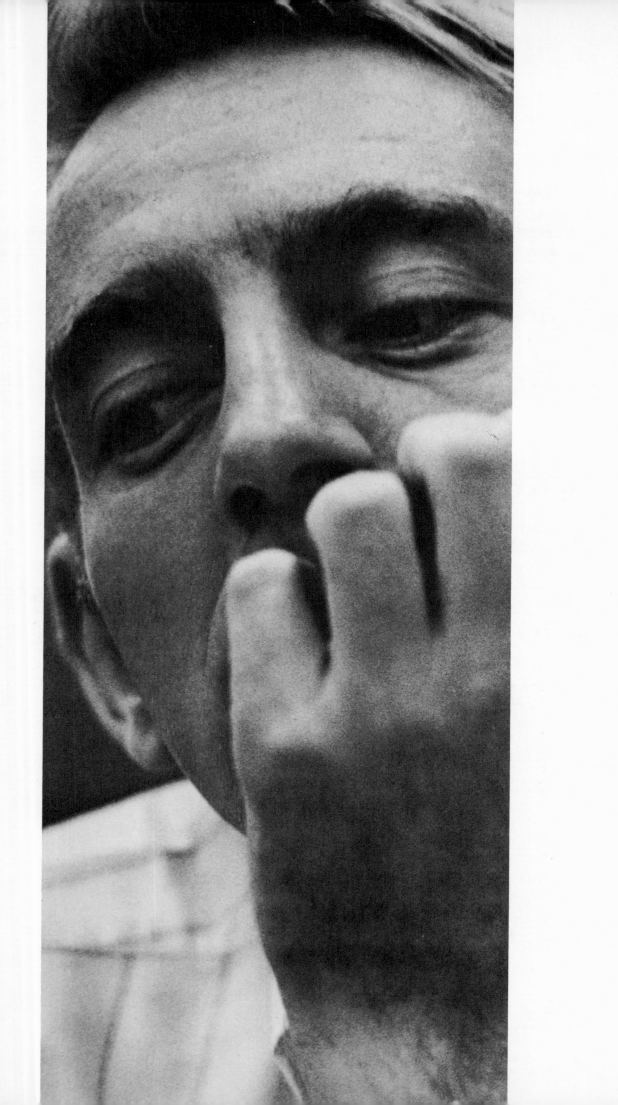

Looking Back at 30

Moderato

1. I lie in some-one's shad - ow and gob - ble up the night, I
run down by the riv - er and watch the wa - ters roll, I'd
thought that time meant noth - ing, I'd use the days like sweets, And
times in some-one's shad - ow, I think I've found a way, To

hide be - hind the dark - ness ____ and hold the mo - ment tight; And ____
let it take my bod - y ____ and e - ven take my soul; For my
pass them out like can - dy ____ all a - long the streets; Ex -
keep the dark - ness for my - self at night as well as day; But ____

just as I'm a man to - mor - row, I'm a man to - night, But
heart is like the riv - er wa - ter, mud - dy, dark and cold, But
chang - ing them for fa - vors from peo - ple that one meets, But
al - ways with the sun - light the shad - ow goes a - way, And

42

LOOK - ING BACK AT THIR - TY, — one thing time has shown, That's
LOOK - ING BACK AT THIR - TY, it's lat - er than I thought, It's
LOOK - ING BACK AT THIR - TY, and old - er by a mile, There've
LOOK - ING BACK AT THIR - TY, — hold - ing back the tears, I

lit - tle con - so - la - tion, When you spend the day a - lone. But
bad to brood the years a - way for what I have - n't got. For
been too man - y stran - gers, that knew my crook - ed smile. And
might as well be one, — two, — three times thir - ty years. But

ev - 'ry day's an - oth - er chance, You've got to dance it like it was the fi - nal

dance; And yet a dance is just a dance and noth - ing more, You can't ex-

pect to turn each turn and find the se - cret door. _____ 2. I

all you touch you can - not keep, And what is love but just an-

oth er kind of sleep; And yet to sleep a - gain would be worth all the trou-bles that I've

known, Some-time I think I'm nev - er ev - er go - ing home. _____ 3. If I

oh, the crowds can be so wild, They push and tram-ple you like

some for-got-ten child; And yet I guess I've nev-er been a child at all,

Ex-cept some-times in terms of feel-ing small. _____ 4. Some

ev-'ry day's an oth-er dance, You got-ta

Love Child

for Robert Fryer

know a-bout his start. While I was grow-in' all the kids would

boast, How their dads was first-est ___ with the most; And

I told sto-ries too ___ a-bout my dad, The base-ball games and fish-ing trips we

had. But I kept play-in' base-ball ___ all a-lone, And a

pain,   Of hav-ing just my ma-ma's _ sec-ond name;   And

from the way she some-times _ looks at me,   I   must be quite a lot like who-

ev - er he may be;   That man who gave his love to her when she was young and wild,   And

left be-hind a leg-a-cy, A lit-tle LOVE   CHILD. _____

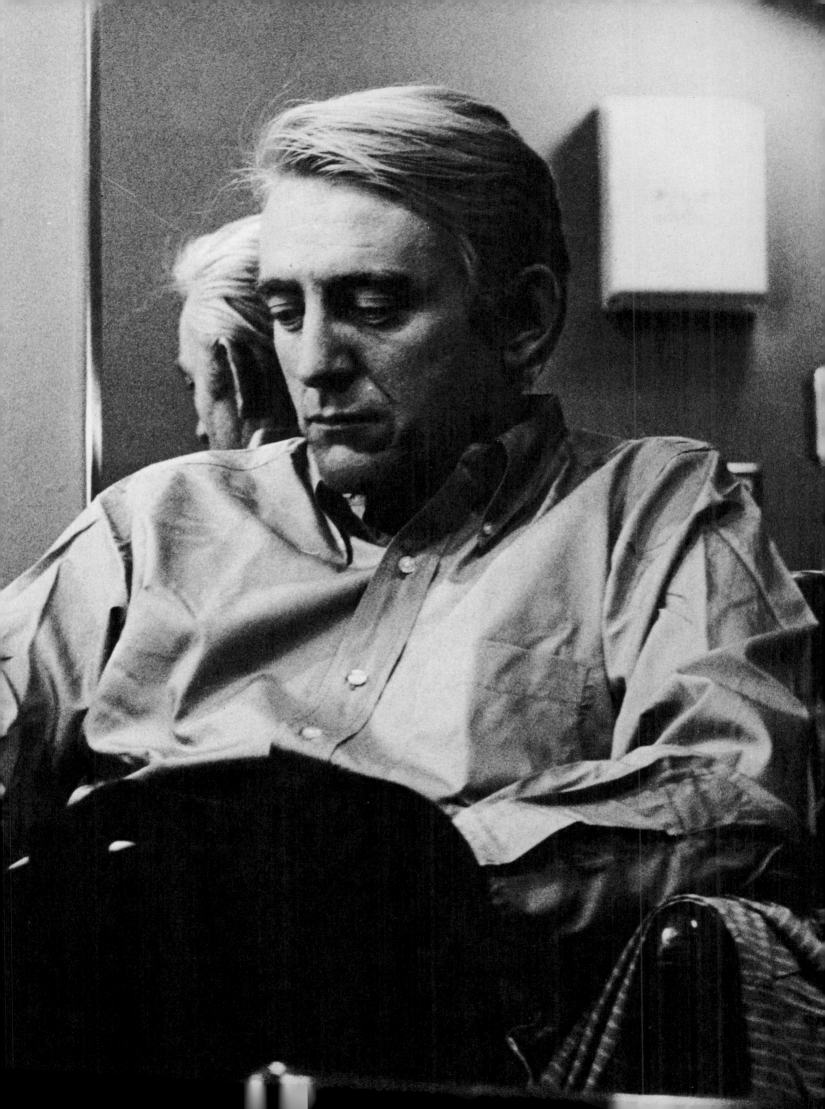

Only Love

Moderato

for Sal and Jo Bonafede

1. We have ON - LY LOVE to of - fer as a prayer,
2. We have ON - LY LOVE to help us find our way,
3. We have ON - LY LOVE to keep us free from harm,

— For all the wrongs — in the world;
— As we go out in - to the world;
As we go a - lone in - to the world; So

So like sing - ing — trou - ba - dours we'll go.
So like laugh - ing chil - dren — we'll go.
on - ly as lov - ers — we'll go.

Sing -ing love— where - ev - er — we go.———————————— ON- LY

I'll Never Be Alone

F Em C F G7 Em Am7
we'll go gen-tle — in the wood; And what we do for one an-oth-er, —
C F C G7 Cmaj7 Dm7(G) Cmaj7
will be warm and good. I'll wear your love, as one might wear a crown of lau-rel
Dm7(G) Em Em7 A7 Dm7
in his hair. And then if you'll be there, I'LL NEV-ER BE — A-
B♭9 A7(♭9) Dm7 Dm7(G) C
LONE, I'll nev-er, ev-er be a-lone.

WHEN FLORA WAS MINE

Slowly

for Neely Plumb

There was sum-mer, there was clo-ver, There was wild __ moun-tain
There were wild deer at the cross-ing, Some-times six __ at a

thyme; There were kids sail-in' kites on the hill-side,
time; There were white puss-y-wil-lows by the riv-er,

1.
When Flo-ra Was Mine.

2.
When Flo-ra Was Mine.

And Flo-ra'd run out a-long the mead-ow, Her hair fly-in' this a-way __ and

69

that a-way — in the wind; Then home with her arms full of blos-soms and branch-es,

To wait for the night to be-gin. Now it's win-ter,

We've grown old-er; Me and the dan-de-li-on wine;

I'm just a fa-ther re-mem-ber-ing the time, When Flo-ra Was Mine.

Ain't You Glad You're Livin', Joe

With a lilt

Leaves are yel-low, ev-'ry girl has got a fel-low, Life is like a mov-ing pic-ture
Sun-burnt nos-es ____ as the sum-mer clos-es, Wait-in' for Oc-to-ber winds to

show; ____ Best Sep-tem-ber I ev-er can re-mem-ber, And
blow; Wad-in' in the o-cean, ____ no more sun-tan lo-tion, ____

1. AIN'T YOU GLAD YOU'RE LIV-IN' JOE.
2. AIN'T YOU GLAD YOU'RE LIV-IN' JOE.

All the lit-tle girls smell so sweet, ____ like sun-shine and sea-weed and

Chasing the Sun

To Coda

One of those bright young men, _____ Run - nin' out aft - er the fun; _____ One of those bright young men, _____ (All) CHAS - ING THE SUN. _____

Coda

_____ How pale they all look in the light of the sun.

Gee, It's Nice to Be Alone

for Frank Sinatra

I Turn to You

85

The Loner

1. I have rid - den rods and bump - ers, Hitched from New York
2. Been as hun - gry as the wind is, Been as thirst - y
3. I have heard the mad mob rag - ing, Lis - tened as they

to L. A., Up from Hous - ton in Oc - to - ber, De -
as the dust; One good rain in Am - a - ril - lo, ___
told their lies; Seen a doz - en lone - some cit - ies, ___

cem - ber down in San - ta Fe. I have walked a hun - dred high - ways
Al - most turned my bones to rust. I have known both light and dark - ness,
Where the sun blacked out the skies. Twen - ty years I've been a Lon - er,

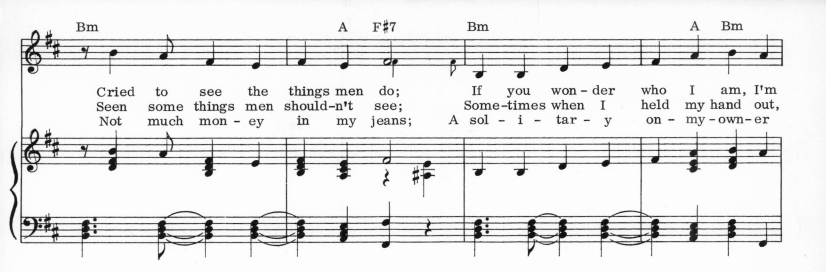

Cried to see the things men do; If you won-der who I am, I'm
Seen some things men should-n't see; Some-times when I held my hand out,
Not much mon-ey in my jeans; A sol-i-tar-y on-my-own-er

tacet.

Just a Lon - er pass - ing through. ____
Peo - ple turned their backs on me. ____
Guess I know what lone - some means. ____

Chorus

You know me, mis - ter, the man with the old suit-

case; You know me, sis - ter, I've

been ev - 'ry - where, Ain't go - in' no - place. ____

D.C.

Fine

90

Methinks Thou Doth Protest Too Much

1. Look at them lit-tle girls in the min-i skirts, ____ Strut-tin' a-round and act-in' like flirts. Show-in' their thigh, ____
2. Look at them hoods ____ on mo-tor-cy-cle bikes, ____ Roar-in' thru the neigh-bor-hood, scar-in' lit-tle tykes. Hell's Lit-tle An-gels ____
3. Look at them lil-y whites go-in' off to church, ____ Lat-er in the aft-er-noon call-in' John Birch. Sound-in' off ____ let-ters to the
4. Look at them pac-i-fists march-in' in the street, Ain't noth-in' much ____ worse than two ____ left ____ feet. Look at them ____ lit-tle kids ____

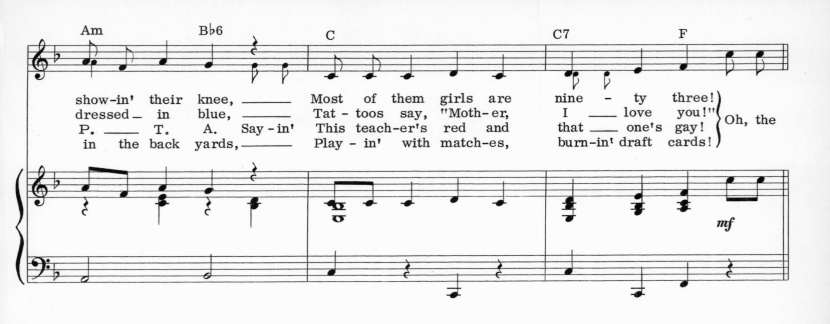

show-in' their knee, _____ Most of them girls are nine - ty three!
dressed _ in blue, _____ Tat - toos say, "Moth- er, I _ love you!"
P. _ T. A. Say - in' This teach-er's red and that _ one's gay!
in the back yards, _____ Play - in' with match-es, burn-in' draft cards!
Oh, the

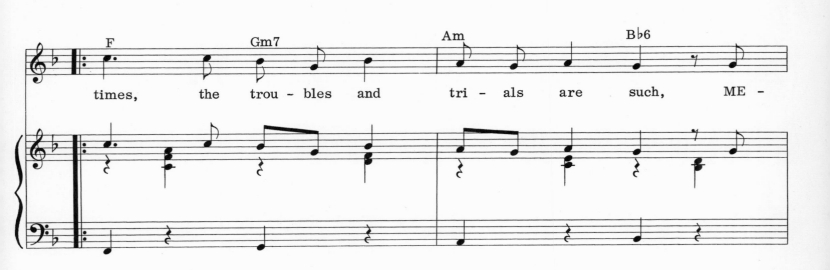

times, the trou - bles and tri - als are such, ME -

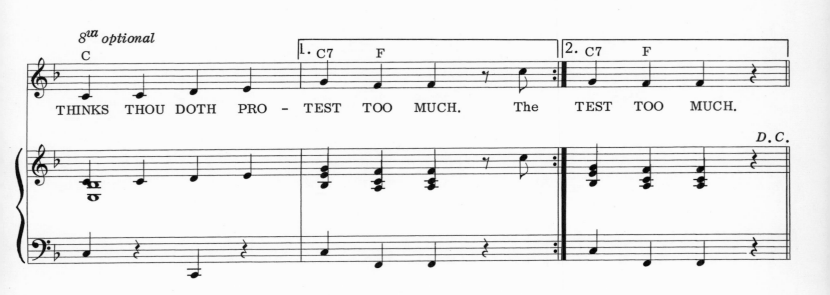

THINKS THOU DOTH PRO - TEST TOO MUCH. The TEST TOO MUCH.

Second Best

Something Beyond

Slowly, with feeling

for Liza Wilke

I've nev - er seen the u - ni-corn at dawn, Be - fore I
(There are some) things I nev-er ev - er said, Some words still

wake up,__ he us-ual-ly has gone, But would I know him if he ev-er came a-
wan-der-ing a-round in-side my head; They lie here wait-ing for the dawn of love to

long, Or think him mere-ly one more__ SOME-THING BE - YOND. There are some
come, Or are they wait-ing for__ SOME-THING BE -

YOND. Be-yond the day, be-yond the day, Be-yond the

The Way It Was Before

for Flo Bennett

Slowly, with feeling

The flow-ers on the hill-side, The kites a-bove the town, The
(The) dap-pled days of danc-ing, The nights too warm to dream, When

skat-ing on the mill-pond, While the snow was fall-ing down; Ah, the years of laugh-ter, but
all the friend-ly an-i-mals would gath-er at the stream; Ah, the end-less sum-mer, but

laugh-ter comes no more, And I wish it was THE WAY IT WAS BE-FORE. The
sum-mer comes no more,

FORE. The way it was when we could talk to one an-oth-er, With words; on-ly

words; And a friend was a friend and a lov - er was a lov - er; And

when you prayed to God, you felt He real - ly heard. The flow - ers all are dy - ing. The

kites are sail - ing down, I guess the friend - ly an - i - mals have

come a - long and gone; I used to wait for sum - mer, but sum - mer comes no more, And I

wish it was THE WAY IT WAS BE - FORE. _____

The Hunters

for Lee Mendelson

hunt - er and the hunt - ed are real - ly quite the same, And the
hunt-ing, not the lov - ing, is the pleas-ure of the game. Don't wor-ry the
wind, _____ did'-nt you know, _____ When the morn-ing
comes, they'll go. _____

1. Fly, bird, they're com-ing and they'll
2. Run, lone-some li - on, don't be

catch you if they can,   _ Lit-tle _ fox, you're not so cun-ning,_
caught, _ fright-ened doe,   They aim their ar - rows straight _ and _ they'll

You can't fool the man. _____   THE HUNT-ERS
cut you down and go. _____   THE HUNT-ERS

turn,   THE HUNT-ERS stare,   _ They would have us all be-
come,   THE HUNT-ERS go   down dark streets danc-ing to the

liev - ing ____ they've real - ly come to care;   _ But just a-cross our
on - ly tunes they know; _____   And the hunt is not for

About the Author

ROD McKUEN was born in Oakland, California, at the end of the Depression. He grew up in California, Nevada, Washington, and Oregon, and worked as a laborer, stunt man, radio disk jockey, and newspaper columnist before serving in the Army in Japan and Korea as a psychological-warfare scriptwriter; he was a member of the Korean Civil Assistance Command.

After he returned home Mr. McKuen was encouraged by his friend Phyllis Diller to perform at San Francisco's Purple Onion. During the engagement he was brought to Hollywood and put under contract to Universal-International as an actor. In 1959 he moved to New York to compose and conduct the music for Albert McCleery's highly lauded television series *The CBS Workshop*.

Mr. McKuen has played the major cabarets and concert halls of the world, and has written more than seven hundred songs. His material has been performed by the leading entertainers and recording artists the world over. Mr. McKuen spends seven months of the year in a house in the Hollywood hills, with a menagerie of cats and dogs, where he does most of his writing. The balance of his time he devotes to traveling and performing in Europe.

With the publication of *Stanyan Street and Other Sorrows* in 1966 and *Listen to the Warm* a year later, Mr. McKuen became the best-selling poet in America. He is currently writing screenplays for both books, and his third volume of poetry, *Lonesome Cities,* has just been published.